Wight Sm
I.O.W CAR...
by

Besley

Most of the cartoons in this collection appeared in the Isle of Wight County Press between 2000 and 2007. A few didn't make it and one or two new ones have been thrown in for good measure.

Acknowledgements -

Thanks as ever to all at Crossprint and the County Press and, for this publication, particular thanks to Robin Freeman, Managing Director of the CP, and Mike Lambert, Designer at Crossprint.

SHANKLIN. I.O.W
as seen by Shanklin folk

CONTENTS

page
4   In the Beginning
5   Fixed Links and Ferries
8   Tourist Trade
11   Watersporting
15   On the Beach
16   Walk the Wight
17   Cycle Wight
18   On the Buses
19   Those Roads
22   All Change
26   Your Council and You
28   Best Days of Your Life
31   Politics
33   Climate Change
35   New Building
36   Closure
38   Oilawoi
40   Tooth and Claw
41   Sport
42   Young and Old
43   Island Rock
45   The Same Each Year

SANDOWN, I.O.W.
as seen by Sandown folk

In the Beginning

MEDIEVAL PAN
(artist's reconstruction,
based on recent
archaeological researches)

ARTIST'S IMPRESSION OF THE
LOST MEDIEVAL VILLAGE OF
NETTLECOMBE

EARLY SUDOKU

Fixed Links and Ferries

A PEEP INTO THE FUTURE:
Construction of the Isle
of Wight Road Bridge

ISLAND BRIDGE

FIRST SAILING ON THE FISHBOURNE - PORTSMOUTH RUN

HOW THE ISLAND KEPT OFF FOREIGN INVASIONS DOWN THE CENTURIES.

HOW TO PARK ON A FERRY:

① Draw up in lane as directed...

② Switch off engine, engaging handbrake, gear, chocks etc for possibility of lively crossing...

③ Acknowledge instruction to move up further 3mm in order to increase acreage of empty deck behind...

④ Bunny-hop into car ahead for cosy crossing.

It is reported that Wightlink's new Yarmouth ferries 'will be able to carry more vehicles... but will be similar in overall size' to existing boats...

Stay in your cars!

[After one ferry failed to stop on reaching the mainland...]

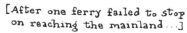

Tourist Trade

THE KIND OF TOURISM THAT
THE ISLAND IS SEEKING TO ATTRACT

A preview of the Island's new visitor sight, the exact centre* of the Isle of Wight.

Watersporting

Not for seagoing, no – just to keep in the drive and impress the neighbours.

A new scheme under consideration to avoid repeats of this year's Round the Island Becalming.

There goes the Fast Cat –

There goes the hover –

There goes Ellen MacArthur –

[COWES WEEK BOBBIES ON BIKES ...]

He snatched my purse and made off that way – in a red Ferrari!

COWES WEEK:

And in answer to your question 'Will anyone this year be brave enough to race ahead of the boss?' –

Nice just to get right away from it all!

LONDON BOAT SHOW

When you said we do all our sailing in the Med, I don't think it was the Medina that he had in mind –

Blast!

On the Beach

Walk the Wight

Cycle Wight

On the Buses

And you're sure this isn't the Punishment Bus we've got on?

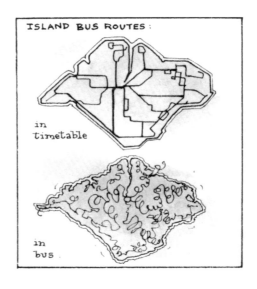

ISLAND BUS ROUTES:

in timetable

in bus

Ever since we had this red surfacing laid in front of the house we've had nothing but buses come thundering down our driveway —

Following news that S Vectis buses are to be given the names of local coastal features...

BUS STOP

Needles!

Those Roads

MORE ISLAND ROAD SIGNS -

Gridlock ahead

Speed camera newly installed

Sleepy village

Festival venue

Yarmouth Bridge stuck again

mini-gridlock

PROPOSED NEW LAYOUT FOR ISLAND ROADS

More signs to look out for following the appearance of the 'Twenty's plenty' signs:

HAIL CHALE

HELLO WELLOW

SLOW YER KNOW

40 Forty's naughty

Flipping Chippings

Bank Holiday Fun as members of the Halfords Car Sponge Owners' Club of Great Britain enjoy a chance encounter with members of the UK Fluffy Dice Owners Club (Northern Branch) during their annual rally tour of the Isle of Wight.

PROPOSED DESIGN
FOR COPPINS BRIDGE

Pedestrianisation
of Newport?

Given their success in dealing with small trouble makers...

Maybe supermarkets could be persuaded to install larger machines...

...for bigger menaces.

Use of Car Horns:

Horns should be sounded only in the following circumstances -

① When recognising someone in the street...

② When saying Goodbye (e.g at end of a long evening)

I believe his job is selling traffic-lights to the Council -

It's really quite quiet for an August Bank Holiday -

All Change

'One third of Island children obese...'

Goggles... helmet... gum-shield -

...gloves... pads ear-plugs chest-protection...

..and all set to CONK -

- ER))

Pssst - do we take euros?

ISLE OF WIGHT ROADS
ARE DIFFERENT...

Your Council and You

THE NEW BROOM
IN COUNTY HALL

Best Days of Your Life

RAISING STANDARDS
IN ISLAND SCHOOLS...

THE BIG EDUCATION DEBATE

Politics

... and I'm your candidate for the Let's - tow-the-Island - further-out -into-the-Channel - and – while-we're-about -it – put - sharks - in-the-Solent Party –

THE BEAUTY CONTEST BEGINS...

We couldn't help noticing you've put down the names of 167 residents for this address on your census form –

Climate Change

And half the time you won't even be able to see them — not when it's nighttime or foggy

'Wind Farms attract tourists' – WOW spokesperson.

SORRY. FULL

SOME OTHER GOOD PLACES FOR WIND·TURBINES

You sure you don't need planning permission?

New Building

Closure

Oilawoi

Crossing the Island's
North-South Divide

LET'S TALK OILAWOI
(with translations in English)
LESSON 4 : BUYING A DRINK —

Aw-roi!
[Good evening, sir]

Aw-roi!
[Evening]

Aw-roi?
[How are you?]

Aw-roi.
[Fine, thanks]

Aw-roi -
[Your usual pint.]

Chiz-may.
[Thank you very much.]

ISLAND-TYPES:
Happy Newcomers

'S brilliant - we love
it here. Apart from the
ferries, of course. And the
roads - the drivers, the
shops, the locals, the prices, the...'

ISLAND-TYPES:

The Seasoned
Traveller

'That's a fair old way
out to Freshwater, you
know.'

Tooth and Claw

SPOTTER'S GUIDE:

razorbill   guillemot

cormorant   shag

piece of wood   dolphin

baby penguin

[A baby penguin went missing from Newchurch...

...and a stork appeared on Sandown/Shanklin golfcourse.]

SQUIRREL IDENTIFICATION CHART:

RED

GREY

FOR NATIONAL PET WEEK A SHORT GUIDE TO LOCAL DOG BREEDS —

WEST ISLAND TERRIFIER

COCKER

ST BONIFACE

BOXER CROSS (VERY)

MINIATURE POODLE

Sport

[Winter Olympics came and went...

...and Curling hit the headlines.]

Young and Old

Now to celebrate with one of your Gran's famous wartime recipes –

Yes, I remember it all as if it were yesterday – the noise, the smoke, the stench...

That ghastly sea crossing, then fighting through bodies to get on the buses –

Buses? Normandy?

I.W. Pop Festival I'm talking about!

REVISING

A peek behind the scenes at Angel Radio...

Island Rock

FOLLOWING THE RECENT SIGHTING OF KATE MOSS IN A SWEETSHOP IN NEWPORT...

MICHAEL SCHUMACHER AT GURNARD...

PAMELA ANDERSON ON THE BEACH AT BINSTEAD

PAVAROTTI ON A BOUNCY CASTLE AT SANDOWN

ELVIS AT HORRINGFORD

Good luck to Ventnor aiming to be capital of Jazz in the deep South...

ALBERT STREET BLUES

STORY LOWTHERVILLE

...and we look forward to others soon following suit —

WELCOME TO BRIGHSTONE HOME OF TAMLA MOORTOWN

CHALE-HOUSE ROCK

ROCKEN ROLL

Sorry, you'll have to speak up a bit —

POP FESTIVAL as envisaged by promoters...

...as envisaged by neighbours

ISLE OF WIGHT FESTIVAL

AMAZING FACTS:

TURNOVER:
£multi-million

ATTENDANCE:
c 35,000 per day

TICKETS EXCHANGED FOR:
up to £300 a pair

RUBBISH:
90 tonnes

TOILETS:
one.

The Same Each Year

Keeps 'em off the streets, I suppose!

Bonfire Night on the IOW...

Other nights on the IOW.

GUY FAWKES UPDATED:

Remember, remember,
From June to December,
Gunpowder, explosions,
the lot.

Great fireworks, eh?

Good ol' Christmas shopping.

POST-CHRISTMAS TRADING